BIRDS

BY

GEORGE B. STEVENSON

 GOLDEN PRESS · NEW YORK

Red-thighed
Falconet

TABLE OF CONTENTS

1969 Edition

© Copyright 1963, 1961, 1959, 1958, 1957, 1956,
1949 by Western Publishing Company, Inc. Pro-
duced in the U.S.A.

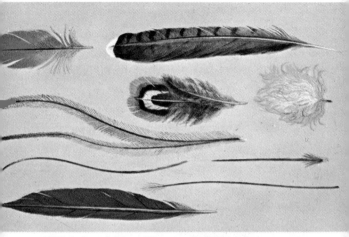

All birds have feathers. These are of different shapes, colors and kinds. No other animals have feathers.

WHAT ARE BIRDS? Birds are warm-blooded, feathered animals that lay eggs. Feathers are of different shapes and uses, and are often colorful. There are three basic kinds of feathers. Soft down feathers keep the bird warm; body feathers give the bird its shape; flight feathers on the wings make flight possible. Some feathers may be modified for special use.

3

Manx Shearwater — soaring flight

Hummingbird—
hovering
flight

Swallow—
gliding flight

Bobwhite —
flapping flight

Most birds can fly. Even those that cannot are descended from ancestors that could. In comparison with the skeletons of other animals, those of birds are lighter. Some of the bones of birds are hollow or are filled with air cells. The ribs are fused to the spine and the keel. The keel is an enlarged breastbone that supports the powerful flight muscles of the chest. Finger bones are fused, and carry the outermost flight feathers.

Flight of Brown Pelican

The wing of a bird has the same shape in cross section as that of the wing of an airplane. It provides lift as the bird, by flapping wings in a power stroke, propels itself forward.

Some birds have mastered the art of soaring. By taking advantage of rising air currents, or of variations in wind speeds at different heights, they fly great distances without flapping a wing.

Skeleton of a bird

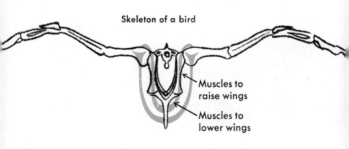

Muscles to raise wings

Muscles to lower wings

5

The Cardinal eats seeds.

Geese eat grain and grass.

FOOD AND FEEDING

Each kind of bird has its own diet, and it is seldom the same as that of another bird. Finches are seed eaters. Geese eat grass, grain, and some water life. Other birds may live almost entirely on the berries or leaves of one kind of tree or shrub. Those that feed only on plants as adults, such as the finches, may feed their young on insects. Pigeons are grain feeders, but the adult birds produce a cheesy material, chemically similar to milk, from their throat lining. The young birds are fed on this until they begin to eat grain. Some other birds feed their nestlings on partly digested food.

Many birds feed entirely upon insects, but even among these insect-eaters different kinds of birds prefer different kinds of insects. Some birds feed on grasshoppers and other ground-dwelling insects; others prey upon insects that feed on leaves. Swallows, swifts, and flycatchers catch flying insects in the air. Woodpeckers dig into tree trunks for the burrowing grubs that live beneath the tree's bark.

Red-headed Woodpecker

Woodpeckers eat grubs.

Flycatchers eat insects.

Scissor-tailed Flycatcher

South American Condor

Meat-eating birds are of two kinds, predators and scavengers. Those that kill for food, such as most eagles and hawks, are predators. They have powerful talons and sharp beaks. The scavengers, such as the vultures, eat dead animals and thus act as a clean-up squad. Gulls are scavengers of the shorelines. Crows and jays feed on fruits and seeds but may also scavenge.

Red-tailed Hawk

Herring Gull

Brown Pelicans eat fish.

Tufted Puffins also eat fish.

Some birds fish for their food. Herons stalk along the shorelines, spearing small fish in the shallows. Terns, kingfishers, and pelicans dive from the air. Gannets and boobies dive from heights of a hundred feet or more into the water, and may swim to depths of one hundred feet. Cormorants, puffins, and loons dive from the surface and swim after fish, while ospreys take fish from the top of the water.

Colorful male finches from Africa, Asia, and Australia

PLUMAGE Each kind of bird has a distinct plumage. Males are usually the more colorful. It is thought that the males' colorful plumage helps them to attract females. The color of the female is often drab, nearly matching the background of the nesting or feeding area. In other species of birds both male and female are colored alike.

Male and female Mandarin Ducks

Male Bird of Paradise

SONG All birds make sounds of distress, alarm, or contentment, but some lack a distinctive song. Among the kinds that sing, the songs have several purposes. Males usually select the area in which the nest will be made and the young raised. Their song warns other males that the territory is occupied. When the females arrive, the males sing to attract them. Males drive away other males that trespass in their territory. Wrens are especially possessive and chase birds much larger than themselves.

Among the singers, the mockingbird is famous, for he imitates other birds.

The Mockingbird, a famous singer, is found in the southern U.S. and Mexico.

Wrens are small but aggressive and noted for their melodious song.

11

Cranes dancing

COURTSHIP Male birds court the females, and each kind has its own courtship pattern. Males may display their plumage, often with song and dance. Males of the Red-Plumed Bird of Paradise hang upside down on a branch, and the long, lacy flank plumes cascade downward. Turkeys and peacocks strut as they display, to impress the females. The rock dove, the pigeon of city parks the world over, prances and coos before the mate of his choice. Many kinds of birds combine courtship displays with song.

The Adelie Penguin offers its mate a pebble.

When males and fe-
males have the same
plumage, their behavior
is different, at least during mating season, and
they may have complex
courtship rituals. The
male Adelie Penguin of-
fers the female a pebble.
If she accepts it, she accepts him as her mate. The

During courtship season the male
Frigatebird's throat pouch is inflated.

cranes dance during their
courtship, but dance at
other times as well. Most
ducks have swimming
dances, bowing, twisting,
and sometimes racing
over the water. Flamingos
and gannets have mass
displays that precede the
actual mating.

The male Lyrebird displaying

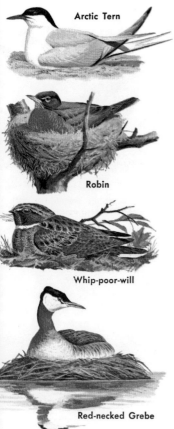

Arctic Tern

Robin

Whip-poor-will

Red-necked Grebe

Hummingbird

NESTING Each kind of bird has its way of making a nest, ranging from a hollow in the sand to the tremendous communal nest which houses several hundred weaver birds.

Sometimes males will help with the nest, but often they do not. Large birds, such as eagles, herons, and hawks, build nests of twigs, while smaller birds weave nests of grass and fibers. Whip-poor-wills nest on the ground. Some waterfowl,

Wagler's Oropendola

Chimney Swift

such as grebes, make rafts of water plants, with a cup-like hollow at the top for the eggs.

Barn and Cliff Swallows build their nests of mud. Woodpeckers dig nest holes in trees.

A few birds, including the Common Cuckoo of Europe and the Cowbird of North America, do not build a nest. The female lays one egg in the nest of another bird, which then hatches it and raises the young bird.

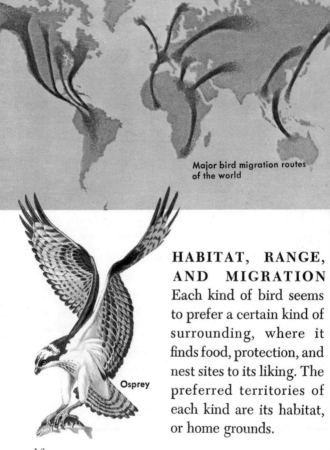

Major bird migration routes of the world

Osprey

HABITAT, RANGE, AND MIGRATION

Each kind of bird seems to prefer a certain kind of surrounding, where it finds food, protection, and nest sites to its liking. The preferred territories of each kind are its habitat, or home grounds.

Ospreys must live near a plentiful supply of fish; their habitat is the edges of large bodies of water. Oceanic birds have the seas for their habitat. Some birds are found only in deserts.

The range of a bird is its geographical distribution. Few birds have world-wide range; most are limited to a much smaller region.

Islands and mountain regions sometimes have kinds of birds that are not found elsewhere. These are descendants of birds that wandered into these regions, lost contact with others of their kind, and developed differently. These new kinds may be limited to a very small range.

Ula-ai-hawane, found only on the Island of Hawaii

17

Arctic Tern

Golden Plover

Birds that spend the year in the same territory are called residents. Those that fly south in winter and north in spring are known as migrants. One of the reasons for the autumn migration is a dwindling food supply, as insects disappear and water freezes into ice. Some birds travel south only a few hundred miles, while others travel great distances. The Arctic Tern migrates as much as 10,000 miles twice yearly. In the fall, Golden Plovers make a nonstop flight from Canada to South America.

In mountainous country, the peaks may be deep in snow while the lower valleys are clear and warm. Many large animals, such as elk and ibex, spend the winter at lower levels, and so do a number of mountain birds. Seed eaters are more likely to migrate up and down mountains with the changing seasons. Insect eaters migrate south for many hundreds of miles to find a supply of food. Ptarmigan, partridge, and grouse are vertical migrants. Mountain Quail, for instance are found at altitudes of up to 7,500 feet in summer, but descend to valleys of less than 5,000 feet in winter. Some kinds of birds migrate east or west from the continent's cold interior to warmer ocean shores. Young birds often wander in all directions after they leave the nest.

Mountain Quail, a vertical migrant

WHERE BIRDS LIVE

PLAINS AND MEADOWS Each type of habitat usually has its own kinds of birds—those that are able to survive and prosper under the special conditions of the area. Birds of open plains and meadows are usually dull in color, and most of them run as well as fly. They nest in the grass, and often conceal their nest and its eggs with great skill. Meadowlarks, Mourning Doves, and Bobwhites are birds of the open country, a habitat they share with such seed eaters as buntings, longspurs, and many of the sparrows.

Bobwhite

Mourning Dove

20

Members of the heron family are common marsh birds.

MARSHES Fresh and salt-water marshes are the home of birds that feed mainly on fish, water insects, and plants. Many marsh dwellers have long legs, and wade through the shallows and the deep grass in search of prey. Others have webbed feet for swimming, and feed while they are floating on the water.

Sandhill Cranes

21

Bluejay

OPEN WOODLANDS

Open woodlands support a variety of birds, as the food supply there is often varied and plentiful. Fruits, berries, insects, and the smaller mammals are most numerous where trees and grassland meet. The most colorful birds of the temperate zones are found in these areas. Man has helped some birds of woodland borders to increase their numbers by opening forests, setting out orchards and by planting trees around homes. These birds are the ones that are most likely to be killed by misuse of chemicals sprayed to kill insect pests.

Cedar Waxwing

Common Snipe

SHORES Birds that live along the shores of oceans and rivers include many kinds of gulls, terns, and ducks. A special group which run and feed along the beach—plovers, sandpipers, and curlews—are known as "shorebirds." These are often found in flocks, feeding upon worms, crabs, and other small animals. Some, like the Killdeer, occur inland where they often search for grubs in plowed fields.

Hudsonian Curlew

Dowitcher

23

Oceanic birds feed on fish, jellyfish, an other forms of floating marine life.

Black-Footed Albatross

Cape Petrel

White-Winged Petrel

Wandering Albatross

Fulmar

Leach's Petrel

OCEANS Oceanic birds spend the greater part of their life at sea. Albatrosses, shearwaters, and petrels come ashore only in the breeding season, usually to remote islands. One of the birds of the ocean, the Wilson's Petrel, may well be the most numerous bird in the world. Many oceanic birds are found south of the Equator, especially in the turbulent seas near the polar regions.

ARCTIC REGIONS The most famous birds of regions of ice and snow are penguins. They are found only in the Southern Hemisphere, where some species breed and raise their young on the Antarctic icecap. Others range as far north as Galapagos Islands. Some ducks and a few sparrows nest in the Arctic.

Emperor Penguin

King Eider

female   male

25

Gould's Sunbird

Macaws

TROPICAL FORESTS Many of the world's most colorful birds dwell in tropical forests. Their gaudy plumage helps to conceal them in their native homes, for, in most cases, the colors are disruptive. This means that the outline of the bird is broken up by patterns of contrasting color. Macaws, sunbirds, motmots, and the Cock-of-the-Rock have the typical brilliant colors of tropical species.

DESERTS True deserts are barren and usually have little or no bird life. In regions of scrub and

Equatorial Cock-of-the-rock   Blue-crowned Motmot

cacti, however, a number of species find a favorable environment especially if there is a spring or water hole nearby. One of the most unusual desert birds is the Roadrunner, a member of the cuckoo family. It feeds on small reptiles, seldom flies, and runs at speeds of 15 miles an hour.

Roadrunner

27

ADAPTATIONS

FEET The shape of a bird's foot is related directly to the habits and habitat of the bird. Predators, suchs as hawks and owls, have strong talons with which they grab their prey. Birds that spend most of their time on the ground have sturdy feet with thick toes. The feet of swimmers are webbed or lobed. Perching birds curl their toes around branches.

Owl — grasping　　Skimmer — walking　　Kiwi — walking　　Finch — per

Coot — swimming　　Ptarmigan — walking in snow　　Woodpecker — climbing　　Hummingbi perchin

NIGHT FLYING Night-hawks, whip-poor-wills, and some related birds live on the insects that fly in the late afternoon and at night. A network of stiff bristles around the mouth helps these birds trap their prey.

Barn Owl

Owls have very keen sight and hearing, and can fly silently. They live on small mammals that are also nighttime feeders.

Common Nighthawk

Although they are normally inactive at night, many kinds of birds fly at night during their annual migrations. They feed and rest in the daytime.

Canvasbacks and Black Ducks dive from the surface to feed on aquatic plants. They swim with their feet, keeping their wings closely folded.

SWIMMING An adaptation is a change in the usual body pattern that permits a better adjustment to a special environment. One such adaptation in birds is the swimming foot. Birds that swim on the surface propel themselves by kicking. Ducks, such as the Common Teal, have webbed feet. Coots have lobed toes.

duck's foot

coot's foot

Birds that swim underwater do so by one of two methods. Cormorants, loons, and some others use their legs and feet; penguins and diving petrel use their wings. Most underwater birds are fish eaters, but a few eat shellfish.

Swimming birds that feed in the water have the legs set far back on the body. This adaptation gives them a more powerful thrust, but makes them awkward or helpless on land. Grebes and cormorants walk with difficulty; loons flounder along their belly. An adaptation that helps in one way may hinder in another.

Petrels are strong, broad-winged birds, not often seen on land. They can fly long distances and are excellent gliders.

Common Diving Petrel

BILLS A bird's bill is a tool for eating, fighting, and nest building. The feeding habits of birds are related directly to the shape of their bills. Sometimes a group of birds—the herons, for example—have similar bills. Sometimes, however, birds that are closely related have different types

HYACINTH MACAW
nutcracker

EVENING GROSBEAK
seed crusher

RED CROSSBILL
pine-cone probe

LETTERED ARICARI
fruit eater

BLACK SKIMMER
surface skimmer

AMERICAN AVOCET
mud probe

of bills because they eat different foods. Thus, the shape of a bird's bill reveals something about what the bird eats and the way in which it gets its food.

American Woodcock probing for earthworm

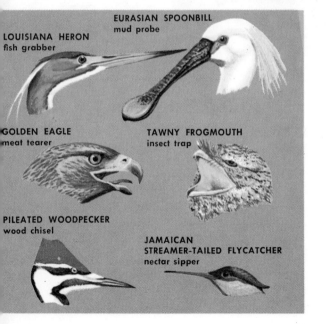

EURASIAN SPOONBILL
mud probe

LOUISIANA HERON
fish grabber

GOLDEN EAGLE
meat tearer

TAWNY FROGMOUTH
insect trap

PILEATED WOODPECKER
wood chisel

JAMAICAN
STREAMER-TAILED FLYCATCHER
nectar sipper

33

Cassowary

Ostrich

FLIGHTLESS BIRDS In addition to feathers, one of the things that sets birds apart from all other warm-blooded animals, except bats, is their power of flight. However, not all living birds can fly, although all of them are descended from flying ancestors. Some non-flying birds are very similar in appearance. Ostriches of Africa, emus of Australia, cassowaries of Australia and New

Guinea, and rheas of South America look very much alike, but their similarities are due more to adaptations to similar environments than to close family relationships. Incidentally, the flightless ostrich is the largest living bird today. Males may be eight feet tall and weigh as much as 300 pounds. They can run as fast as 30 miles per hour.

Penguins cannot fly. Among the many other flightless species are one or more members of each of the following families; cormorant, parrot, rail, duck, grebe, and wren. The chicken-sized Kiwi of New Zealand is another species that has lost the use of its wings. A number of other birds are weak flyers, and some day their descendants may be flightless.

Kiwi

ORNAMENTAL BIRDS In many lands, man has given special meanings to the plumage of some birds. Aztec and Mayan Indians used the plumes of the male Quetzal in religious ceremonies.

Tail plumes of Peacocks (the male Peafowl— the female is a Peahen) were one of the symbols of royalty in the Orient. This bird has been partly domesticated, and is now fairly common.

Quetzal   Peacock

Ring-necked Pheasant

Golden Pheasant

Some kinds of birds are kept for their ornamental value. Swans, geese, and ducks are kept in park ponds. Storks and cranes, most often seen in zoos, are sometimes found in estate gardens. Pheasants, which are native to Asia, are often raised as ornamental birds. The kinds usually raised are the Ring-necked, the Golden, and the Lady Amherst. Doves, especially the colorful species from Australia and southeastern Asia, are sometimes kept for their beauty. Toucans do well in captivity. Some of the varieties of domestic chickens are also show birds.

Members of the parrot family are usually easily tamed and are popular cage birds.

CAGE BIRDS The birds that are kept for pets are called cage birds. They are valued for their colorful plumage, their song, or their intelligence. Some respond to the affection and company of humans and some birds are great mimics.

The most popular cage birds are the parrots, and their relatives, the parakeets, lories, lorikeets, cockatoos, cockateels, and macaws.

Canary

One of the most popular cage birds is the Canary, a small, yellow finch originally from the Canary Islands off the coast of Africa. They were introduced into Europe as pets by Spanish sailors. The wild birds are more green than yellow, but selective breeding has developed the bright yellow hue. Canaries are noted for their singing, for which captive birds are also bred.

The Hill Mynah mimics a variety of sounds, including whistles, mechanical sounds, and the human voice, with startling accuracy. It is a starling, and eats insects and fruits.

BLUE PARAKEET

ALBINO PARAKEET

HARLEQUIN PARAKEET

GREEN PARAKEET

GAME BIRDS Where hunting is unrestricted, any edible bird may be killed and eaten. In the regions that are heavily populated by humans, the bird population must be protected from over-hunting. Some birds, known as game birds, may be hunted, at certain seasons of the year, while most others are protected by law at all times.

Game birds usually include edible waterfowl (ducks and geese), the chicken-like birds (turkeys, pheasants, grouse, and quail), doves and pigeons, woodcock, snipe, and a few others.

Refuges have been established for migrating ducks.

Bobwhites are popular game birds in some areas of the U.S.

Some nations have special biologists, trained in the study of wildlife conservation, who determine which game birds are raising enough young to allow the hunters to take a yearly harvest. Whenever the numbers of one kind of game bird drop too low, the biologists place it on the protected list—which means it cannot be hunted.

More and more countries all over the world are realizing that their wild life should be conserved for the benefit and enjoyment of all.

41

California Condor

THREATENED BIRDS Perhaps eighty kinds of birds of the world are in danger of extinction. Another nineteen have not been seen in recent years, and have probably become extinct. In some cases, these birds were already dying out when man-made changes in their environment, such as the cutting of forests and drainage of swamp regions, finally doomed them. Some of the ones that survive in limited numbers are the Whooping Crane and California Condor, the Flamingo and the White Stork.

White Stork

West Indian Flamingo

Ivory-billed Woodpecker   Passenger Pigeon

EXTINCT BIRDS About forty kinds of birds are known to have become extinct in the past three hundred years. Some, such as the Passenger Pigeon and the Labrador Duck, have been hunted and possibly exterminated by man. Some could not adapt to a changing world. The Ivory-billed Woodpecker, for example, now thought to be extinct, apparently could not survive the destruction of southern forests since it ate only larvae found in dead trees.

Some Breeds of Chickens

BUFF MINORCA

PLYMOUTH ROCK
(Barred)

PLYMOUTH ROCK
(Silver Penciled)

MOTTLED HOUDAN

BUFF LEGHORN

WHITE LEGHORN

All illustrations Courtesy
of the *Poultry Tribune*

DOMESTIC BIRDS

Man learned how to keep and raise certain birds in captivity long before he learned to write. Ancestors of the barnyard chicken were wild jungle fowl in southeast Asia. Domestic ducks came from the wild ducks of Europe. The domestic turkey is nearly the same as the wild birds of North and Central America. Each kind of domestic bird has been improved by careful breeding, and furnishes more meat and eggs than its wild cousins. Some hens for instance now lay 300 eggs a year.

EVOLUTION OF BIRDS Evidence from fossils and from the study of living animals shows that birds have evolved from one group of reptiles—probably from lizard-like creatures with long hind legs that lived about 180 million years ago. Most living birds still have scaled legs. Feathers and reptilian scales have a common origin. The fingers of birds' ancestors became modified into bones in the wingtips, but the young of one living bird, the Hoatzin, have two claws on each wing.

Birds are warm-blooded and have no teeth, while reptiles are cold-blooded and most of them have teeth. The similarities between the two groups are most obvious in their skeletons. Both have the same general skeletal

The young Hoatzin uses the claws on its wings for climbing. The claws disappear after two or three weeks.

Archaeopteryx, the oldest known bird

plan, but that of the bird has many modifications for flight. Somewhere between the early reptiles and the modern birds is Archaeopteryx. Its skeleton, found in rocks that are 150 million years old, shows that it had teeth and a very simple tail.

QUIZ-ME

Here are some questions you can answer if you have studied this book on birds. Pages where the answers will be found are listed at the end.

1 Are birds the only warm-blooded animals that fly?
2 Name two birds that dive into water for their food.
3 What bird do some people think to be the most numerous bird in the world?
4 Are a bird's flight muscles in its wings, its back, or its chest?
5 From what animals did birds probably evolve?
6 Do all birds fly?
7 Do vultures, gulls, and other scavengers have any value?
8 Have the songs of birds any purpose?
9 Do all birds build nests?
10 What bird migrates as much as 10,000 miles twice a year?
11 Have man's activities helped to increase the numbers of some birds?
12 Name two birds that stay at sea for months.
13 Are penguins found only in the Antarctic?

14 Does colorful plumage endanger the bird that wears it?

15 Do birds that swim underwater use their wings or their legs?

16 What is the largest living bird?

17 Are all non-flying birds closely related?

18 Did canaries get their name because they are canary yellow?

19 Can game birds be shot at any time of the year?

20 What is the difference between a predator and a scavenger?

21 Were all the extinct birds killed off by man?

22 Do all swimmers have webbed feet?

23 What is the food of herons?

24 Name two night-flying birds.

25 Do all birds sing?

ANSWERS: 1 (p. 34), **2** (p. 9), **3** (p. 24), **4** (p. 4), **5** (p. 45), **6** (p. 34), **7** (p. 8), **8** (p. 11), **9** (p. 15), **10** (p. 18), **11** (p. 22), **12** (p. 24), **13** (p. 25), **14** (p. 26), **15** (p. 30), **16** (p. 35), **17** (p. 35), **18** (p. 39), **19** (p. 40), **20** (p. 8), **21** (p. 43), **22** (p. 30), **23** (p. 9), **24** (p. 29), **25** (p. 11).

ILLUSTRATIONS BY: *Dorothea and Sy Barlowe, James Gordon Irving, Matthew Kalmenoff, William de J. Rutherfoord, Arthur Singer.* COVER BY: *Robert Candy*

A